4-Chord Songbook

More Acoustic Hits

£9 1/68

GW00569332

WISE PUBLICATIONS
part of The Music Sales Group
London / New York / Paris / Sydney / Copenhagen / Berlin / Madrid / Tokyo

This *4-Chord Songbook* allows even beginner guitarists to play
and enjoy the best acoustic hits. The songs have been specially arranged
so that only 4 chords are needed to play all of the songs in the book.

The *4-Chord Songbook* doesn't use music notation. Throughout
the book chord boxes are printed at the head of each song; the
chord changes are shown above the lyrics. It's left to you,
the guitarist, to decide on a strum pattern or picking pattern.

Some of the arrangements indicate that a capo should be
used at a particular fret. This is to match the song to the key of
the original recording so that you can play along; otherwise the capo
is not needed for playing on your own. However, if the pitch of
the vocal line is not comfortable for singing (if it is pitched too high
or too low) you may wish to use a capo anyway; placing the
capo behind a suitable fret will change the key of the song
without learning any new chords.

Whatever you do, this *4-Chord Songbook* guarantees hours
of enjoyment for guitarists of all levels, as well as providing
a fine basis for building a strong repertoire.

Published by
Wise Publications
14-15 Berners Street, London W1T 3LJ, UK.

Exclusive Distributors:
Music Sales Limited
Distribution Centre, Newmarket Road, Bury St Edmunds, Suffolk IP33 3YB, UK.
Music Sales Pty Limited
120 Rothschild Avenue, Rosebery, NSW 2018, Australia.

Order No. AM992695
ISBN 978-1-84772-445-8
This book © Copyright 2007 Wise Publications,
a division of Music Sales Limited.

Printed in the EU.

www.musicsales.com

Relative Tuning

The guitar can be tuned with the aid of pitch pipes or dedicated electronic guitar tuners which are available through your local music dealer. If you do not have a tuning device, you can use relative tuning. Estimate the pitch of the 6th string as near as possible to E or at least a comfortable pitch (not too high, as you might break other strings in tuning up). Then, while checking the various positions on the diagram, place a finger from your left hand on the:

5th fret of the E or 6th string and **tune the open A** (or 5th string) to the note (A)

5th fret of the A or 5th string and **tune the open D** (or 4th string) to the note (D)

5th fret of the D or 4th string and **tune the open G** (or 3rd string) to the note (G)

4th fret of the G or 3rd string and **tune the open B** (or 2nd string) to the note (B)

5th fret of the B or 2nd string and **tune the open E** (or 1st string) to the note (E)

E	A	D	G	B	E
or	or	or	or	or	or
6th	5th	4th	3rd	2nd	1st

Head

Nut

1st Fret

2nd Fret

3rd Fret

4th Fret

5th Fret

Reading Chord Boxes

Chord boxes are diagrams of the guitar neck viewed head upwards, face on as illustrated. The top horizontal line is the nut, unless a higher fret number is indicated, the others are the frets.

The vertical lines are the strings, starting from E (or 6th) on the left to E (or 1st) on the right.

The black dots indicate where to place your fingers.

Strings marked with an O are played open, not fretted. Strings marked with an X should not be played.

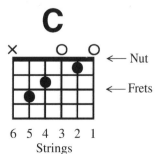

C

← Nut

← Frets

6 5 4 3 2 1
Strings

Angel Of Harlem

Words & Music by
U2

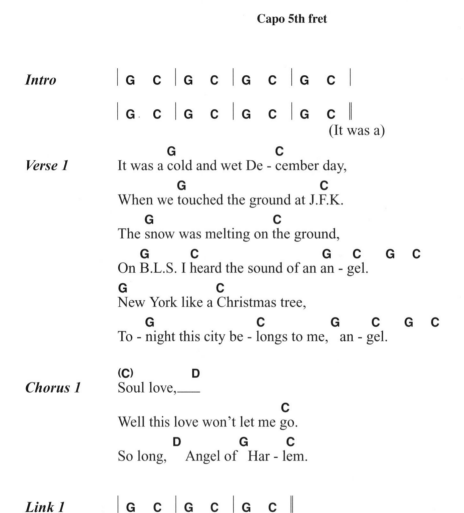

G   C   D   Em

Capo 5th fret

Intro
| G   C | G   C | G   C | G   C |

| G. C | G   C | G   C | G   C ‖
                                (It was a)

Verse 1
```
          G                    C
It was a cold and wet De - cember day,
          G                    C
When we touched the ground at J.F.K.
     G                    C
The snow was melting on the ground,
     G        C              G   C   G   C
On B.L.S. I heard the sound of an an - gel.
G               C
New York like a Christmas tree,
     G              C            G   C   G   C
To - night this city be - longs to me,   an - gel.
```

Chorus 1
```
     (C)          D
Soul love,___

                        C
Well this love won't let me go.
          D        G   C
So long,    Angel of  Har - lem.
```

Link 1
| G   C | G   C | G   C ‖

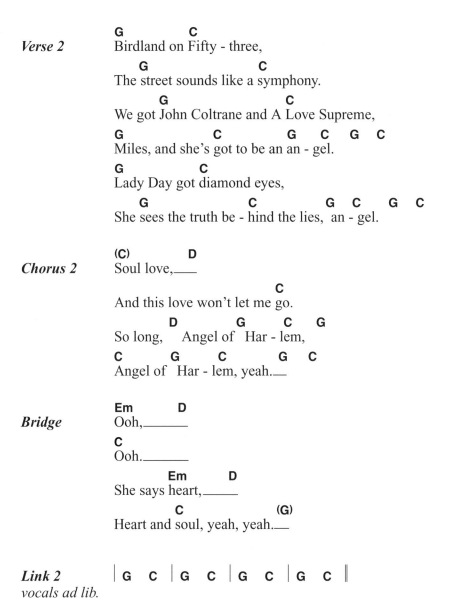

Verse 2

```
        G          C
Birdland on Fifty - three,
           G                    C
The street sounds like a symphony.
             G                  C
We got John Coltrane and A Love Supreme,
G              C           G   C   G   C
Miles, and she's got to be an an - gel.
G             C
Lady Day got diamond eyes,
           G                  C          G   C   G   C
She sees the truth be - hind the lies,  an - gel.
```

Chorus 2

```
     (C)          D
Soul love,____

                          C
And this love won't let me go.
           D       G     C   G
So long,    Angel of  Har - lem,
C      G     C        G   C
Angel of  Har - lem, yeah.____
```

Bridge

```
Em          D
Ooh,_____

C
Ooh._____

          Em       D
She says heart,_____

           C              (G)
Heart and soul, yeah, yeah.____
```

Link 2
vocals ad lib.

```
|G  C |G  C |G  C |G  C ‖
```

Verse 3

G   C
Blue light on the avenue,

G   C
God knows they got to you.

G   C
Empty glass, the lady sings,

G   C
Eyes swollen like a bee-sting.

G   C
Blinded, you lost your way,

  G   C
In side streets and the al - leyways.

          G   C
Like a star exploding in the night,

G   C
Falling to the city in broad daylight.

Chorus 3

(C)
Angel in devil's shoes,

D
  Salvation in the blues.

                        C   D
You never looked like an angel, yeah, yeah.__

          G   C
Angel of Har - lem.

Link 3 | G C | G C | G C ‖

Outro

       G   C   G
‖: An - gel,__

C   G   C G   D
Angel of Har - lem.   :‖ *Repeat to fade*

Every Morning

Words & Music by
Mark McGrath, Rodney Sheppard, Murphy Karges, Stan Frazier, Craig Bullock,
David Kahne, Joseph Nichol, Richard Bean, Abel Zarate & Pablo Tellez

Capo 1st fret

Intro

| (D) | (C) | (G) | (C) (D) |
| G D | C D | G D | C D |

Verse 1

```
      G                   D        C
      Every morning there's a halo hanging
          D      G                D   C   D
From the corner of my girlfriend's four-post bed,
G                D           C
   I know it's not mine but I'll see if I can use it
D     G                D    C
For the weekend or a one-night stand.
D      G          C            G   C
Couldn't understand   how to work it out,
          G                       C
Once a - gain as predicted left my broken heart open
                G         C
And you ripped it out.
G                       D
Something's got me reeling,
C                       D
Stopped me from believ - ing,
G         D     C   D
Turn me a - round a - gain.
G                  D
Said that we can do it,
    C              D    G
You know I wanna do it a - gain.
```

Chorus 1

    D
(Sugar Ray say)

G   **C**
Oh, _____ (every morning,)

     G
Oh, _____ (every morning

     C   **D**
⎰ When I wake up.)
⎱   (Shut the door baby, don't say a word.)

Oh, _____

G   **C**
(She always rights the wrongs,)

     G   **C**   **D**
⎰ (She always rights, she always rights.)
⎱   (Shut the door baby, shut the door baby.)

Link | **G**   **D** | **C**   **D** | **G** | **C**   **D** ||

Verse 2

    G   **D**   **C**
    Every morning there's a heartache hanging

            D   **G**   **D**   **C**   **D**
From the corner of my girlfriend's four-post bed,

G   **D**   **C**   **D**
   I know it's not mine and I know she thinks she loves me,

     G   **D**   **C**   **D**
But I never can believe what she said.

G   **D** **C**   **D**
Something so deceiv - ing when you stop believ - ing,

G   **D**   **C** **D**
Turn me a - round a - gain.

G   **D**
Said we couldn't do it,

     C   **D** **G**
You know I wanna do it a - gain.

Chorus 2

G   **C**
Oh, _____ (every morning,)

     G
Oh, _____ (every morning

     C   **D**
⎰ When I wake up.)
⎱   (Shut the door baby, don't say a word.)

8

cont.
           G   **C**   **D**
Oh, _____ (every morning,)

              G
Oh, _____ (every morning

                C   **D**
{ When I wake up.)
          (Shut the door baby, shut the door baby.)

Bridge
          C   **D**   **G**   **Em**
She always rights the wrongs for me, ba - by.
          C   **D**   **G**
She always rights the wrongs for me.

Verse 3
                    D   **C**
Every morning there's a halo hanging
                  D   **G**   **D** **C** **D**
From the corner of my girlfriend's four-post bed,
          G   **D**   **C**   **D**
 I know it's not mine but I'll see if I can use it
            G   **D** **C**
For the weekend or a one-night stand.

Chorus 3
                                  D
(Shut the door baby, don't say a word.)
          ‖: **G**   **D**   **C** **D**
    Every morn - ing,
          G   **D**
   Every morn - ing,
              C   **D**
When I wake up.
          (Shut the door baby, shut the door baby.) :‖ *Repeat to fade*
                                                       with vocal ad lib.

Destiny Calling

Words & Music by
Tim Booth, Jim Glennie, Saul Davies, Mark Hunter & David Baynton-Power

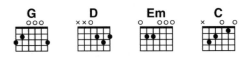

Capo 2nd fret

Verse 1

N.C.   G   D   Em
So we may be gorgeous, so we may be famous,

C   G   D   Em
Come back when we're getting old.

C   G   D   Em
Cover us in chocolate, sell us to the neighbours,

C   G   D Em
Frame us in a video.

C   G   D   Em
Clone us in a test tube, sell us to the multitude,

C   G   D   Em
Guess that's the price of fame.

C   G   D   Em
She likes the black one, he likes the posh one,

C   G   D Em
Cute ones are usually gay.

Chorus 1

C   G   D   Em C
Here we come, this is our destiny calling,

       G   D   Em C
We're freaks, this is our destiny calling.

     G D   Em C   G D Em
U - nique, this is our destiny calling now.

Verse 2

C   G   D   Em
Don't believe the adverts, don't believe the expert,

C   G   D   Em
Everyone will sell our souls.

C   G   D   Em
Get a little wiser, get a little humble,

C   G   D   Em
Now we know that we don't know.

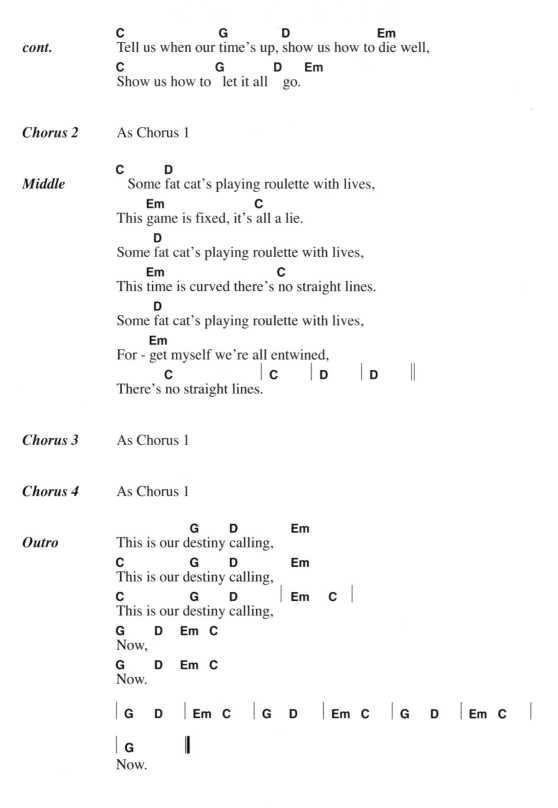

cont.

    C   G   D   Em
Tell us when our time's up, show us how to die well,

    C   G   D   Em
Show us how to   let it all   go.

Chorus 2   As Chorus 1

Middle

    C   D
  Some fat cat's playing roulette with lives,

      Em   C
This game is fixed, it's all a lie.

      D
Some fat cat's playing roulette with lives,

      Em   C
This time is curved there's no straight lines.

      D
Some fat cat's playing roulette with lives,

      Em
For - get myself we're all entwined,

        C | C | D | D ||
There's no straight lines.

Chorus 3   As Chorus 1

Chorus 4   As Chorus 1

Outro

            G   D   Em
This is our destiny calling,

    C   G   D   Em
This is our destiny calling,

    C   G   D | Em   C |
This is our destiny calling,

G   D   Em C
Now,

G   D   Em C
Now.

| G   D | Em C | G   D | Em C | G   D | Em C |

| G ||
Now.

Hey, That's No Way To Say Goodbye

Words & Music by
Leonard Cohen

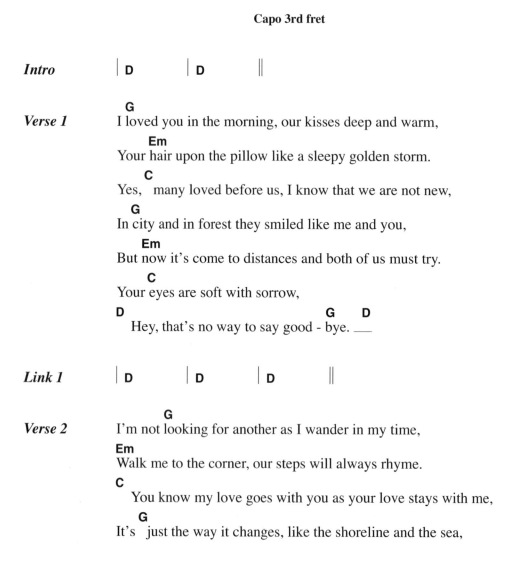

D **G** **Em** **C**

Capo 3rd fret

Intro | D | D ‖

Verse 1
    G
I loved you in the morning, our kisses deep and warm,
      Em
Your hair upon the pillow like a sleepy golden storm.
     C
Yes,   many loved before us, I know that we are not new,
     G
In city and in forest they smiled like me and you,
      Em
But now it's come to distances and both of us must try.
     C
Your eyes are soft with sorrow,
D   **G**   **D**
    Hey, that's no way to say good - bye. __

Link 1 | D | D | D ‖

Verse 2
     G
I'm not looking for another as I wander in my time,
Em
Walk me to the corner, our steps will always rhyme.
C
    You know my love goes with you as your love stays with me,
     G
It's   just the way it changes, like the shoreline and the sea,

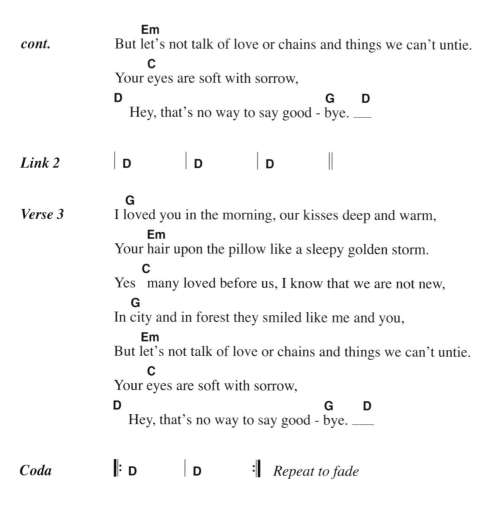

cont.

      Em
But let's not talk of love or chains and things we can't untie.

      C
Your eyes are soft with sorrow,

D   **G**   **D**
    Hey, that's no way to say good - bye. ___

Link 2 | **D** | **D** | **D** ||

Verse 3

      G
I loved you in the morning, our kisses deep and warm,

        Em
Your hair upon the pillow like a sleepy golden storm.

      C
Yes   many loved before us, I know that we are not new,

      G
In city and in forest they smiled like me and you,

       Em
But let's not talk of love or chains and things we can't untie.

      C
Your eyes are soft with sorrow,

D   **G**   **D**
    Hey, that's no way to say good - bye. ___

Coda   ‖: **D** | **D**   :‖ *Repeat to fade*

In The Air Tonight

Words & Music by
Phil Collins

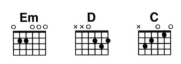

Tune guitar down by a tone

Intro | Em   D | C   D | Em   D | C   D ||

Chorus 1
    Em   **D**   **C**   **D**
    I can feel it coming in the air to - night, oh Lord,
    Em   **D**   **C**   **D**
    And I've been waiting for this moment for all of my life, oh Lord.
    Em   **D**   **C**   **D**   **Em**
    Can you feel it coming in the air to - night, oh Lord, oh Lord.

Verse 1
    (Em)
    Well if you told me you were drowning

    D
    I would not lend a hand.

       C
    I've seen your face before, my friend,

         D
    But I don't know if you know who I am.

         Em
    Well, I was there and I saw what you did,

    D
    Saw it with my own two eyes,

         C
    So you can wipe off that grin, I know where you've been,

      D
    It's all been a pack of lies.

Chorus 2
    Em   **D**   **C**   **D**
    And I can feel it coming in the air to - night, oh Lord,
    Em   **D**   **C**   **D**
    Well I've been waiting for this moment for all of my life, oh Lord.
    Em   **D**   **C**   **D**
    I can feel it coming in the air to - night, oh Lord,
    Em   **D**   **C** **D**   **Em**
    And I've been waiting for this moment for all of my life, oh Lord, oh Lord.

Verse 2

(Em)   **D**
Well I remember, I remember, don't worry,

                             C
How could I ever forget the first time,

                  D
The last time we ever met.

          Em   **D**
But I know the reason why you keep the silence up,

No you don't fool me.

   C
The hurt doesn't show, but the pain still grows,

          Em
It's no stranger to you or me.

Chorus 3

(Em)   **D**   **C**   **D**
  And I can feel it coming in the air to - night, oh Lord,

Em   **D**   **C**   **D**
  Well I've been waiting for this moment for all of my life, oh Lord.

Em   **D**   **C**   **D**
  I can feel it in the air tonight, oh Lord, oh Lord,

Em   **D**   **C**   **Em**
  But I've been waiting for this moment for all of my life, oh Lord.

Chorus 4

(Em)   **D**   **C**   **D**
‖: I can feel it coming in the air to - night, oh Lord,

Em   **D**   **C**   **D**
  And I've been waiting for this moment all of my life, oh Lord.

Em   **D**   **C**   **D**
  I can feel it in the air tonight, oh Lord, oh Lord, oh Lord

Em   **D**   **C**   **D**
  Well I've been waiting for this moment for all of my life, oh Lord. :‖

Repeat to fade
with vocal ad lib.

Foundations

Words & Music by
Kate Nash & Paul Epworth

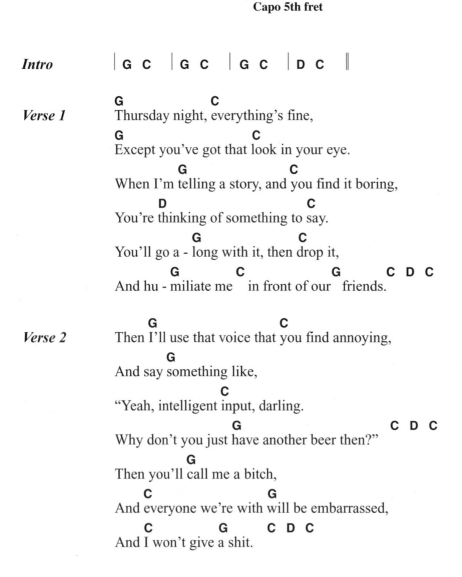

Capo 5th fret

Intro | G C | G C | G C | D C ‖

Verse 1
G   C
Thursday night, everything's fine,
G   C
Except you've got that look in your eye.
          G   C
When I'm telling a story, and you find it boring,
          D   C
You're thinking of something to say.
          G   C
You'll go a - long with it, then drop it,
          G   C   G   C D C
And hu - miliate me   in front of our   friends.

Verse 2
          G   C
Then I'll use that voice that you find annoying,
          G
And say something like,
              C
"Yeah, intelligent input, darling.
              G   C D C
Why don't you just have another beer then?"
          G
Then you'll call me a bitch,
          C   G
And everyone we're with will be embarrassed,
          C   G   C D C
And I won't give a shit.

Chorus 1

        C   Em
My fingertips are holding onto the cracks in our foundation,

          D   C
And I know that I should let go, but I can't.

           Em   D
And every time we fight I know it's not right,

                                 C
Every time that you're upset and I smile,

                          D
I know I should forget, but I   can't.

Verse 3

        G   C   G   C
You said I must eat so many lemons   'cause I am so bitter.

        G   C
I said: "I'd rather be with your friends, mate,

        D   C
'Cause they are much fit - ter."

        G   C
Yes, it was childish and you got aggressive,

        G   C   G
And I must admit that I was a bit scared,

                         C   D   C
But it gives me thrills to wind you up.

Chorus 2   As Chorus 1

Verse 4

        G   C
Your face is pasty,

            G   C   G
'Cause you've gone and got so wasted, what a sur - prise!

                 C   D   C
Don't want to look at your face,   'cause it's making me sick.

        G   C   G
You've gone and got sick on my trainers,

           C   G
I only got these yester - day.

                C   D   C
Oh my gosh,   I cannot be bothered with this.

        G   C
Well, I'll leave you there till the morning,

           G   C
And I purposely won't turn the heating on,

           G   C   D   C
And dear God, I hope I'm not stuck with this one.

Chorus 3   As Chorus 1

Chorus 4

              C   **Em**
And every time we fight I know it's not right,

                                    D
Every time that you're upset and I smile,

                           C
I know I should forget, but I can't.

       Em   **D**
And every time we fight I know it's not right,

                                 C
Every time that you're upset and I smile,

                           D
I know I should forget, but I   can't.

Outro | **C** | **Em** | **D** | **C** |

               | **Em** | **D** | **C** | **D** | **Em**   ‖

New Slang

Words & Music by
James Mercer

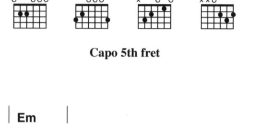

Capo 5th fret

Intro　　| Em　| Em　|

|: Em G　| C G　| D G　| Em D :| *Repeat 4 times*

| G　| G　|

Verse 1

Em　　　　　G　　　　　C　　　　G　　　D
Gold teeth and a curse for this town, were all in my mouth.
　　　　　G　　　　　C　　　　　Em D
Only, I don't know how they got out, dear.
Em　　　　　G　　　C G　　　　　D
Turn me back into the pet I was when we met.
　　　　　G　　　C　　　　　Em　D
I was happier then with no mind-set.

Chorus 1

　　　　　　　　　　D　　　G
And if you'd took to me like
　　　C　　G　　　　　　　D
A　　gull takes to the wind.
　　　　　　　　　　　　　　G
Well, I'd have jumped from my trees,
　　　C　　　G　　　　　C　　　　G
And I'd have danced like the king of the eyesores,
　　　C　　　G　　　　　　D
And the rest of our lives would have fared well.

Verse 2

Em   G   C   G   D
New slang when you notice the stripes, the dirt in your fries.

        G   C   Em D
Hope it's right when you die, old and bo - ny.

Em   G   C
Dawn breaks like a bull through the hall,

   G   D
Nev - er should have called,

      G   C   Em D
But my head's to the wall and I'm lone - ly.

Chorus 2

        D   G
And if you'd took to me like

    C   G   D
A gull takes to the wind.

             G
Well, I'd have jumped from my tree,

    C   G   C   G
And I'd have danced like the king of the eyesores,

     C   G   D
And the rest of our lives would have fared well.

Guitar solo 1 $\frac{2}{4}$| D G |

      $\frac{4}{4}$| C G |

      $\frac{2}{4}$| C G |

      $\frac{4}{4}$| D G |

      $\frac{2}{4}$| D G |

      $\frac{4}{4}$| C |

       | C G |

      $\frac{2}{4}$| C G |

      $\frac{4}{4}$| D G | Em D | G | G   ‖

Verse 3

    Em   G   C   G   D
Godspeed all the bakers at dawn, may they all cut their thumbs,

          G   C   Em   D
And bleed into their buns till they melt a - way.

                 G   C   G   D
I'm looking in on the good life I might be   doomed never to find.

                    G   C G   D
Without a trust or flaming fields am I too dumb to re - fine?

Chorus 3

                D   G
And if you took to me like...

        C   G   C   G
Well, I'd have danced like the queen of the eyesores,

          C   G   D
And the rest of our lives would have fared well.

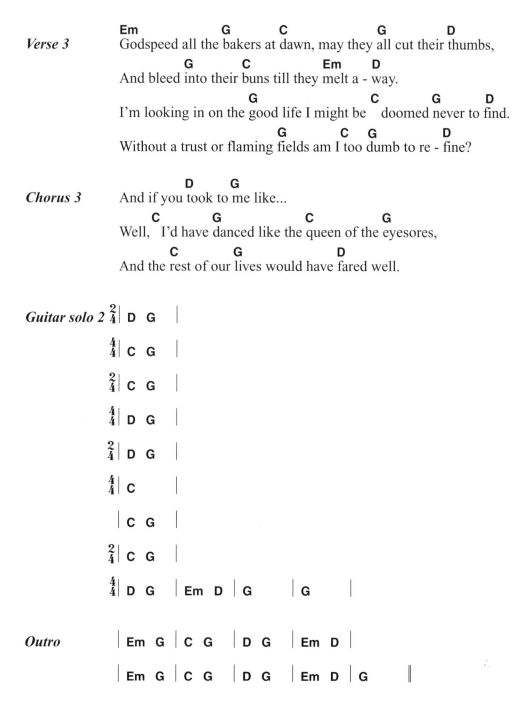

Guitar solo 2 $\frac{2}{4}$| D G |

            $\frac{4}{4}$| C G |

            $\frac{2}{4}$| C G |

            $\frac{4}{4}$| D G |

            $\frac{2}{4}$| D G |

            $\frac{4}{4}$| C |

              | C G |

            $\frac{2}{4}$| C G |

            $\frac{4}{4}$| D G | Em D | G | G |

Outro | Em G | C G | D G | Em D |

                | Em G | C G | D G | Em D | G   ‖

Not Fade Away

Words & Music by
Charles Hardin & Norman Petty

Capo 2nd fret

Intro
‖ D G D | D G D | D G D | D G D ‖

Verse 1
D   G |G C G|
I wanna tell you how it's gonna be,
D   G D |D G D|
You're gonna give your love to me,
D   G |G C G‖
I'm gonna love you night and day.

Chorus 1
        D   G D |D G D|
Well, love is love and not fade a - way,
        D   G D |D G D‖
Well, love is love and not fade a - way.

Verse 2
        D   G |G C G|
And my love is bigger than a Cadil - lac,
D   G D |D G D|
I'll try to show it if you drive me back.
        D   G |G C G|
Your love for me has got to be real,
        D   G D |D G D‖
Before you'd have noticed how I   feel.

Chorus 2

```
D               G  D  | D   G  D |
Love real not fade a - way,
        D            G  D  | D   G  D ‖
Well love real not fade a - way,      yeah!
```

Instrumental

```
| G   C  G | G   C  G | D   G  D | D   G  D |

| G   C  G | G   C  G | D   G  D | D   G  D | D   G  D ‖
```

Verse 3

```
D                        G  | G   C  G |
I wanna tell you how it's gonna be,
D                   G  D   | D   G  D |
You're gonna give your love to  me,
D                        G  | G   C  G ‖
Love that lasts more than one day.
```

Chorus 3

```
    D                   G  D  | D   G  D |
Well love is love and not fade a - way,
       D                G  D  | D   G  D |
Well love is love and not fade a - way,
    G                    D  | G   D   |
Well love is love and not fade a - way,
       D                G  D | D   G  D
‖: Well love is love and not fade a - way.          :‖ Repeat to fade ad lib.
```

23

Oh My Sweet Carolina

Words & Music by
Ryan Adams

G   C   D   Em

Capo 7th fret

Intro

| G | G | G | G |

Verse 1

      G
Well I went down to Houston,

    C   G
And I stopped in San Antone.

                        D
I passed up the station for the bus.

    C   G
I was trying to find me something,

  Em   D   C
But I wasn't sure just what.

     G   D   G
Man, I ended up with pockets full of dust.

Verse 2

    G   C   G
So I went on to Cleveland and I ended up insane,

                                  D
I bought a borrowed suit and learned to dance.

 C   G
   And I was spending money

        Em   D   C
Like the way it likes to rain.

     G   D   G
Man, I ended up with pockets full of cane.

Chorus 1

       Em   C   G
Oh my   sweet Caro - lina,

Em   C   D
   What com - pels me to go?

       Em   C   G
Oh my   sweet dispo - sition,

        G   D   C
May you one day carry me home.

Instrumental 1 | G |G |G |G   ‖

Verse 3

```
       G                             C                 G
I ain't never been to Vegas but I gambled of my life,
                                         D
Building newsprint boats I race to sewer mains.
   C              G            Em    D      C
Was trying to find me something but I wasn't sure just what,
   G              D                G
Funny how they say that some things never change.
```

Chorus 2   As Chorus 1

Instrumental 2 | Em   C |G | Em   C |D |

                  |Em   G |G | G   D   C   G |C |

                  |G |G |G |G   ‖

Verse 4

```
   G                          C                  G
Up here in the city feels like things are closing in,
                                   D
The sunset's just my light bulb burning out.
   C              G            Em    D      C
  I miss Ken - tucky and I miss my fami - ly,
       G              D                G
All the sweetest winds they blow across the south.
```

Chorus 3

```
       Em    C          G
Oh my     sweet Caro - lina,
   Em            C          D
  What com - pels me to go?
       Em  C          G
Oh my     sweet dispo - sition,
           G      D        C
May you one day carry me home.
           Em    D      G    C
May you one day carry me home.
```

Outro |Em   D |G   C |Em   D |G   C |G   ‖

Peace Train

Words & Music by
Cat Stevens

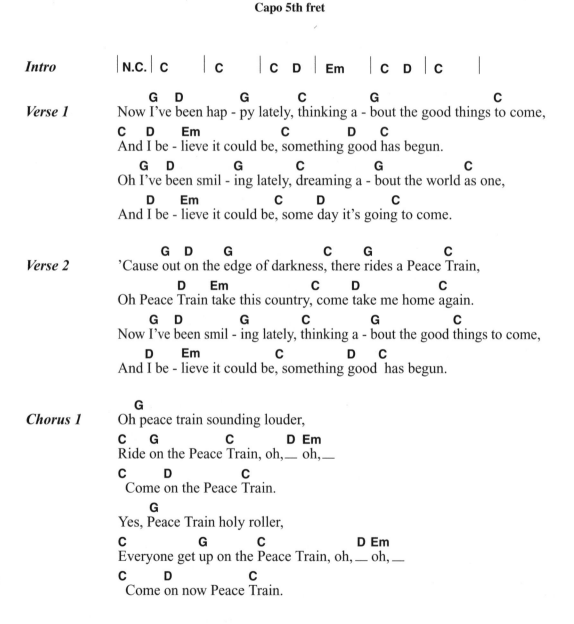

Capo 5th fret

Intro | N.C. | C | C | C D | Em | C D | C | |

Verse 1
G D   G   C   G   C
Now I've been hap - py lately, thinking a - bout the good things to come,
C   D   Em   C   D   C
And I be - lieve it could be, something good has begun.
G D   G   C   G   C
Oh I've been smil - ing lately, dreaming a - bout the world as one,
D   Em   C   D   C
And I be - lieve it could be, some day it's going to come.

Verse 2
G D   G   C   G   C
'Cause out on the edge of darkness, there rides a Peace Train,
D   Em   C   D   C
Oh Peace Train take this country, come take me home again.
G D   G   C   G   C
Now I've been smil - ing lately, thinking a - bout the good things to come,
D   Em   C   D   C
And I be - lieve it could be, something good has begun.

Chorus 1
                  G
Oh peace train sounding louder,
C   G   C   D Em
Ride on the Peace Train, oh,— oh,—
C   D   C
 Come on the Peace Train.

                  G
Yes, Peace Train holy roller,
C   G   C   D Em
Everyone get up on the Peace Train, oh, — oh, —
C   D   C
 Come on now Peace Train.

Verse 3

```
        G  D   G              C    G                C
Get your bags together, gonna bring your good friends too,
           D       Em       C  D       C
'Cause it's get - ting nearer, it soon will be with you.
         G   D   G          C   G        C
And come and join the living, it's not so far from you,
           D       Em      C     D    C
And it's get - ting nearer, soon it will all be true.
```

Chorus 2

```
          G
Oh Peace Train sounding louder,
C     G            C         D Em
Ride on the Peace Train, oh, __ oh, __
C      D          C
 Come on the Peace Train.
```

```
| G   | G   | C G C | C  D  | Em  | C  D | C   ‖
```

Verse 4

```
        G   D      G          C         G            C
Now I've been cry - ing lately, thinking a - bout the world as it is,
          D     Em        C   D     C
Why must we go on hating, why can't we live in bliss?
           G  D   G            C    G           C
'Cause out on the edge of darkness, there rides a Peace Train,
             D       Em        C     D         C
Oh Peace Train take this country, come take me home again.
```

Chorus 3

      G
Oh Peace Train sounding louder,

C   G   C   D Em
Ride on the Peace Train, oh,— oh,—

C   D   C
Come on the Peace Train.

         G
Yes, Peace Train holy roller,

C   G   C   D Em
Everyone get up on the Peace Train, oh,— oh,—

C   D   C
Come on, come on, come on,

D   Em
Come on, Peace Train,

C   D   G |C G C|C D|Em ‖
   Yes it's the Peace Train?   Oh,— oh.—

C   D   C   G |C G C‖
Come on the Peace Train, the Peace Train.

Outro |C D|Em|C D|Em ‖
        Oh,— oh.—

    ‖: C |C |C |C   :‖ *Repeat ad lib.*

    |G |G |D |C |

    ‖: G |Em |Em |C D :‖ *Repeat to fade*

Rhiannon

Words & Music by
Stevie Nicks

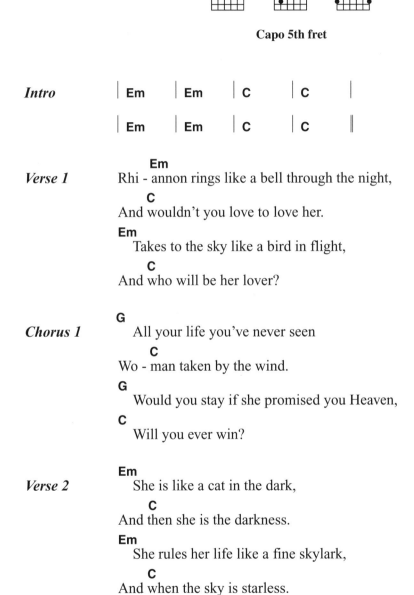

Capo 5th fret

Intro

| Em | Em | C | C | |

| Em | Em | C | C | |

Verse 1

   Em
Rhi - annon rings like a bell through the night,

  C
And wouldn't you love to love her.

Em
  Takes to the sky like a bird in flight,

  C
And who will be her lover?

Chorus 1

 G
  All your life you've never seen

   C
Wo - man taken by the wind.

 G
  Would you stay if she promised you Heaven,

 C
  Will you ever win?

Verse 2

  Em
  She is like a cat in the dark,

   C
And then she is the darkness.

  Em
  She rules her life like a fine skylark,

   C
And when the sky is starless.

Chorus 2

G
All your life you've never seen

C
Wo - man taken by the wind.

G
Would you stay if she promised you Heaven,

C
Will you ever win,

Will you ever win?

Bridge

| Em | Em   C | Em
          Rhian - non,

C   Em
Rhian - non,

C   Em
Rhian - non,

C
Rhian - non.

Verse 3

Em
She rings like a bell through the night,

C
And wouldn't you love to love her.

Em
She rules her life like a bird in flight,

C
And who will be her lover?

Chorus 3

G
All your life you've never seen

C
Wo - man taken by the wind.

G
Would you stay if she promised you Heaven,

C
Will you ever win,

Will you ever win?

| C | C |

Bridge 2

| Em | Em C | Em
                  Rhian - non,

     C Em
Rhian - non,

     C Em
Rhian - non,

C   Em
Taken by, taken by the sky.

C   Em
Taken by, taken by the sky.

C   Em
Taken by, taken by the sky.

| C | C |

Guitar solo

||: Em | Em | C | C |

| Em | Em | C | C :||

Outro

Em
||: Dreams unwind,

                    C
Love's a state of mind... :|| *Repeat to fade*

Save Tonight

Words & Music by
Eagle-Eye Cherry

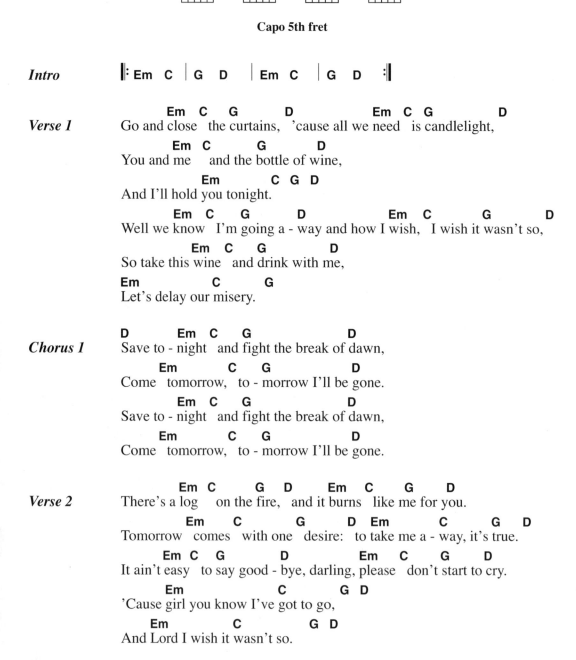

Capo 5th fret

Intro ‖: Em C │ G D │ Em C │ G D :‖

Verse 1
       Em C G   D   Em C G   D
Go and close the curtains, 'cause all we need is candlelight,
       Em C   G   D
You and me   and the bottle of wine,
                Em   C G D
And I'll hold you tonight.
       Em C   G   D   Em C   G   D
Well we know I'm going a - way and how I wish, I wish it wasn't so,
           Em C   G   D
So take this wine and drink with me,
Em   C   G
Let's delay our misery.

Chorus 1
D   Em C   G   D
Save to - night and fight the break of dawn,
       Em   C G   D
Come tomorrow, to - morrow I'll be gone.
       Em C   G   D
Save to - night and fight the break of dawn,
       Em   C G   D
Come tomorrow, to - morrow I'll be gone.

Verse 2
       Em C   G D   Em C   G   D
There's a log   on the fire, and it burns like me for you.
           Em   C   G   D Em   C   G D
Tomorrow comes with one desire: to take me a - way, it's true.
       Em C G   D   Em   C   G   D
It ain't easy to say good - bye, darling, please don't start to cry.
       Em   C   G D
'Cause girl you know I've got to go,
       Em   C   G D
And Lord I wish it wasn't so.

Chorus 2   As Chorus 1

Solo   ‖: Em C │ G D │ Em C │ G D :‖

                      Em   C   G   D

Verse 3   To - morrow comes to take me a - way,

                Em   C   G   D

          I wish that I, that I could stay.

                Em   C   G D

          Girl you know I've got to go,

                          Em   C   G D

          Oh, and Lord I wish it wasn't so.

Chorus 3   As Chorus 1

Chorus 4   As Chorus 1

                Em C   G   D

Coda   ‖:   To - morrow I'll be gone,

                Em C   G   D

                    To - morrow I'll be gone. :‖

Solo   ‖: Em C │ G D :‖   *Play 3 times*

        │ Em C │ G D ‖: Em C │ G D :‖ *Repeat to fade*

                Save to - night.   Save to -

'74-'75

Words & Music by
Mike Connell

Em   G   D   C

Capo 4th fret

Intro | Em G D | Em | Em G D | Em ||

Verse 1

     C   G   C
    Got no reason for coming to me
         G   D   C
And the rain running down.
             G   Em
There's no reason.
  C   G   C
    And the same voice coming to me
        G   D   C
Like it's all slowing down.
         G   D
And be - lieve me:

Chorus 1

        Em   G
I was the one who let you know,
         D   C
I was your sorry-ever-after.
        Em   G   D
Seventy-four, seventy-five.

Verse 2

     C   G   C
    It's not easy, nothing to say
        G   D   C
'Cause it's al - ready said.
       G   Em
It's never easy.
       C   G
When I look on your eyes,
     Em   G   C
Then I find that I'll do fine.
      Em   G   D
When I look on your eyes then I'll do better.

Chorus 2

     Em   **G**   **D**   **C**
I was the one who let you know, I was your sorry-ever-after.

     Em   **G** **D**
Seventy-four, seventy-five.

       Em   **G**   **D**   **C**
Giving me more and I'll defy, 'cause you're really only after

     Em   **G** **D**
Seventy-four, seventy-five.

Guitar solo | **Em** **G D** | **Em** | **Em** **G D** | **Em** | **G** **D** |

            | **Em** | **G** **D** | **Em** | **G** **D** | **Em** **C** | **G** **D** ||

Verse 3

    C   **G**   **C**
   Got no reason for coming to me

     G   **D**   **C**
And the rain running down,

     G   **Em**
There's no reason.

       C   **G**
When I look on your eyes,

     Em   **G**   **C**
Then I find that I'll do fine.

     Em   **G**   **D**
When I look on your eyes then I'll do better.

Chorus 3

     Em   **G**   **D**   **C**
I was the one who let you know, I was your sorry-ever-after.

     Em   **G** **D**
Seventy-four, seventy-five.

       Em   **G**   **D**   **C**
Giving me more and I'll defy, 'cause you're really only after

     Em   **G** **D**
Seventy-four, seventy-five.

Chorus 4   As Chorus 3

                                       Repeat to fade

Coda ||: **Em** **G** | **D** **C** | **Em**   **G** | **D**   :||

             (Seventy-four, seventy-five.)

Sheila

Words by Jim Parker, Jamie Treays & John Betjeman
Music by Jim Parker & Jamie Treays

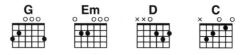

Chorus 1

G   Em
Sheila goes out with her mate Stella,

                     D
It gets poured all over her fella,

                            C
'Cause she says, "Man he ain't no better

                       G
Than the next man kicking up fuss."

                         Em
Drunk, she stumbles down by a river,

                 D
Screams calling "London."

                   C   G
None of us heard her coming; I guess the carpet weren't rolled out.

Interlude

G
Oh when my love, my darling,

          Em
You've left me here alone,

        D
I'll walk the streets of London,

           C
Which once seemed all our own.

         G
The vast suburban churches,

          Em
To - gether we have found:

              D
The ones which smelt of gaslight,

          C
The ones in incense drowned.

Verse 1

G
Her lingo went from the Cockney to the Gringo,

Em
Anytime she sing a song the other girls sing along.

D
And tell all the fellas that the lady is single,

C
A fickle way ta tickle on my young man's ting.

G
She's up for doing what she like, any day, more like the night!

Em
She drowned drunk the sorrows, that she stole, bought, borrowed.

D
She didn't like fights but at the same time understood that,

C
Fellas will be fellas till the end of time.

Link 1

G
Good heavens you boys,

Em
Blue-blooded murder of the English tongue!

D   **C**
Blup!

Verse 2

G   **Em**
Jack had a gang that he called the Many Grams,

D
He was known as Smack Jack the Cracker man.

C
In life he was dealt some shit hands,

G
But the boys got the back now.

Em
And Jay went the same way as Micky and Dan,

D
Dependent man's upon the he - roin.

C
And man, Lisa had a baby with Sam,

And now Jack's on his own man.

G
Well done, Jack! Glug Down that cider,

Em
You're right – she's a slut and you never fucking liked her.

D
Not like, what, he stopped so shocked,

C
'Cause it turns out the last dance killed the pied piper.

cont.

G
Tough little big man, friends with your daughters,

Em
Only 'cause they drive him to pick up all his quarters.

D   **C**
Crawler, lager lout brawlers, fall to the floor think they're free,

But they ain't near da border.

G
Too young gunned down are by your hell fire corner,

Em
Always did a favour but never took a order.

    D
Be - have young scallywag! A fine young Galahad,

C
Glad-ragged up, but only ever getting fag hags.

G
Hung on his shoulder, cheap price shop tag,

Em
Slag better understand he came for the glamour.

    D
But this town's original, superficial the issue,

    C
For one dear Jack had thirty-five doppelgangers.

Chorus 2   As Chorus 1

Link 2
N.C.
It's over man, it's over! LONDON!

Verse 3
    G
So this a short story about the girl Georgina,

Em
Never seen her worse, clean young mess,

    D
Under stress at best, but she's pleased to see you.

    C
With love, God Bless, we lay her body to rest.

    G
Now it all dear started with Daddy's alcoholic,

Em
Lightweights, chinking down, numbing his brain.

    D
And the doctor said he couldn't get the heart dear started,

cont.

    C
Now beat up, drugged up, she feeling the strain.

      G
She says, "In a rut, what the fuck I supposed to do?"

Em
Suck it up, start, stop, keep running through.

D
"True, but you try, it ain't easy to do."

     C
She been buckle-belt, beaten from the back like a brat,

G
Dunno where she going, but she know where she at.

    Em
So Georgie, it's time to chain react,

     D
But the truth is, you know, she probably fought back.

C
Tears stream down her face, she screamed away:

G
"When I fall, no one catch me,

Em   **D**
Alone, lonely, I'll overdose slowly, get scared, I'll scream and shout."

     C
But you know it won't matter she'll be passing out.

   G
I said giggidibidup, just another day,

     Em
An - other sad story that's tragedy.

    D
Para - medic announced death at ten thirty,

C
Rip it up, kick it, to spit up the views.

Chorus 3   As Chorus 1

Chorus 4   As Chorus 1

The Sound Of Silence

Words & Music by
Paul Simon

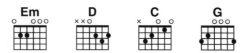

Tune guitar down by a semitone

Intro | **Em** ||

Verse 1

Em   **D**
    Hello, darkness, my old friend,
                                Em
I've come to talk with you a - gain.
                      C   **G**
Because a vision soft - ly creep - ing,
                     C   **G**
Left its seeds while I was sleep - ing.
           C
And the vision
                     G
That was planted in my brain

Still remains
             D   **Em**
Within the sound of silence.

Verse 2

N.C.   **D**
In restless dreams I walked a - lone,
                      Em
Narrow streets of cobble - stone.
                  C   **G**
Beneath the halo of a street lamp,
                    C   **G**
I turned my collar to the cold and damp.
            C
When my eyes were stabbed,
                 G
By the flash of a neon light

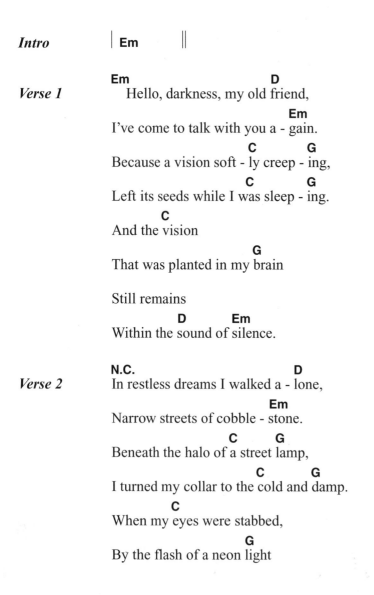

cont.

                      Em
That split the night
G   D   Em
  And touched the sound of silence.

Verse 3

                      D
And in the naked light I saw
                      Em
Ten thousand people, maybe more:
                C   G
People talking with - out speak - ing,
                C   G
People hearing with - out list - 'ning,
            C   G
People writing songs that voices never share,
              Em
And no-one dare
G   D   Em
  Disturb the sound of silence.

Verse 4

                      D
"Fools," said I, "You do not know,
                  Em
Silence like a cancer grows.
                C   G
Hear my words that I might teach you,
                C   G
Take my arms that I might reach you."
          C   G   Em
But my words like silent raindrops fell,
      G   D   Em
And echoed in the wells of silence.

Verse 5

                      D
And the people bowed and prayed,
                Em
To the neon god they made.
                C   G
And the sign flashed out its warn - ing,
                C   G
In the words that it was form - ing.
                C
And the sign said, "The words of the prophets
                G
Are written on the subway walls,
                Em
And tenement halls,
      G   D   Em
And whispered in the sounds of silence."

Stand By Me

Words & Music by
Ben E. King, Jerry Leiber & Mike Stoller

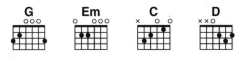

Capo 2nd fret

Intro | N.C.(G) | (G) | (Em) | (Em) |

| (C) | (D) | (G) | (G) ||

Verse 1
         G
When the night has come,
Em
   And the land is dark,
       C   **D**   **G**
And the moon is the only light we'll see.

No, I won't be afraid,
      Em
Oh, I won't be afraid,
       C   **D**   **G**
Just as long as you stand, stand by me.

So darling, darling:

Chorus 1
(G)
Stand by me,
     Em
Oh, stand by me,
   C   **D**   **G**
Oh, stand,   stand by me,   stand by me.

Verse 2

G
If the sky that we look upon,

Em
   Should tumble and fall,

    C   **D**   **G**
Or the mountain should crumble to the sea.

    G
I won't cry, I won't cry,

      Em
No, I won't___ shed a tear,

    C   **D**   **G**
Just as long as you stand, stand by me.

And darling, darling:

Chorus 2

(G)
Stand by me

    Em
Oh, stand by me

   C   **D**   **G**
Whoa, stand now,   stand by me,   stand by me.

Instrumental   ‖: G | G | Em | Em |

                | C | D | G | G   :‖

                                            2° And darling, darling:

Chorus 3

     G
‖: Stand by me,

    Em
Oh, stand by me,

    C   **D**   **G**
Oh, stand now, stand by me, stand by me.

Whenever you're in trouble won't you stand by me,

    Em
Oh, stand by me,

    C   **D**   **G**
Whoa, stand now, oh, stand, stand by me.

Darling, darling: :‖ *Repeat to fade ad lib.*

43

There Is A Mountain

Words & Music by
Donovan Leitch

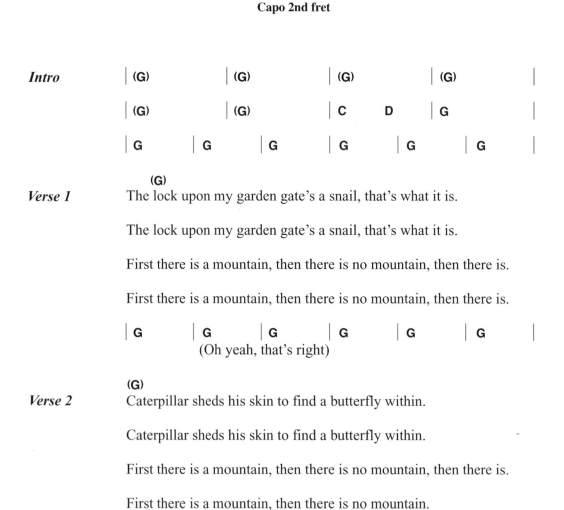

Capo 2nd fret

Intro | (G) | (G) | (G) | (G) |

| (G) | (G) | C   D | G |

| G | G | G | G | G | G |

Verse 1

(G)
The lock upon my garden gate's a snail, that's what it is.

The lock upon my garden gate's a snail, that's what it is.

First there is a mountain, then there is no mountain, then there is.

First there is a mountain, then there is no mountain, then there is.

| G | G | G | G | G | G |
(Oh yeah, that's right)

Verse 2

(G)
Caterpillar sheds his skin to find a butterfly within.

Caterpillar sheds his skin to find a butterfly within.

First there is a mountain, then there is no mountain, then there is.

First there is a mountain, then there is no mountain.

Bridge

                      (G)   Em
Oh Juanita, oh Juanita, oh Juanita, I call your name.
                      G
Oh, the snow will be a blinding sight to see

As it lies on yonder hillside.

Verse 3

                      (G)
The lock upon my garden gate's a snail, that's what it is.

The lock upon my garden gate's a snail, that's what it is.

Caterpillar sheds his skin to find a butterfly within.

Caterpillar sheds his skin to find a butterfly within.

| G | G | G | G | |
| G | G | G | G | |

Verse 4

                      (G)
‖: First there is a mountain, then there is no mountain, then there is.

First there is a mountain, then there is no mountain, then there is.

First there is a mountain, then there is no mountain, then there is.

First there is a mountain, then there is no mountain, then there is. :‖

Repeat to fade

Vice

Words & Music by
Johnny Borrell

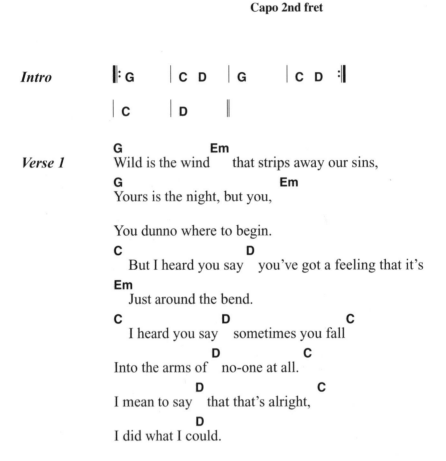

Capo 2nd fret

Intro

‖: G | C D | G | C D :‖

| C | D ‖

Verse 1

G   Em
Wild is the wind   that strips away our sins,
G   Em
Yours is the night, but you,

You dunno where to begin.
   C   D
    But I heard you say   you've got a feeling that it's
Em
    Just around the bend.
   C   D   C
    I heard you say   sometimes you fall
                 D   C
Into the arms of   no-one at all.
               D   C
I mean to say   that that's alright,
               D
I did what I could.

Chorus 1

```
          G    C          D      G
          Oh,   sometimes I run and
                             C D
          Yeah, sometimes I fall  but if it's
          G          C          D
          L-O-V-E, I'll,  I'll see you later,
          G          C          D
          L-O-V-E, I'll,  I'll see you later.
```

Link 1

```
          | G         | G        | Em        | Em  C  D ‖
```

Verse 2

```
          G            Em
          Yours is the fire     that gets in my head,
          G                   Em
          Mine is desire, so let it,

          Well, let it burn down your bed.
                    C
          'Cause I    heard about those stories,
          D                         Em
          Yeah, I guess everyone has.
          C                    D                     C
           And I heard them say    sometimes you fall,
                               D            C
          Just on your own with    no-one at all.
                          D            C
          I mean to say    that that's alright,
                          D
          I did what I could.
```

Chorus 2   As Chorus 1

Link 2 | Em   D | Em C D ‖

Chorus 3   As Chorus 1

Outro

```
G              C      D
  L  -  O  -  V  -  E
G        .     C      D
  L  -  O  -  V  -  E
```

```
G                    C                D
L-O-V-E, L-O-V-E, yes I'll see you later,
                G
I'll see you some - time.
                            C
I'll see you there, I'll see you there,
                    D
But you know, you know, you know
      G                C      D
You can't touch love with a   cynical feeling,
          G                    C        D
No you   can't touch love, but you   do be - lieve.
     G            C      D
Oh la la la love is no   cynical feeling,
           G                            C
I'll see you later, see you sometime, some - time,
             D
You know, it's just like that
G
   Sometimes you run, sometimes you fall
                   D                    G
Sometimes you cry, sometimes you're high,
```

Ring my number back it's
```
     C           D                 G
Oh, seven, seven, six, one, oh, one, oh,   two, three, three.
     C
Oh ring it number one,
       D
We'll ring you right back,
       G
We'll ring you right back,
```

We'll ring you right back,
```
       C
We'll ring you right back,
G
That's just life.
```

```
| Em  D  | Em  C  D ‖
```